ROYAL
CONSERVATORY OF MUSIC

University of Toronto

GRADE II

PIANOFORTE
EXAMINATION

ISBN 0-88797-032-X

The Frederick Harris Music Co. Limited

529 Speers Road, Oakville, Ontario, Canada L6K 2G4

Printed in Canada

FOREWORD

This book, published by authority of the Royal Conservatory of Music, contains a selection of pieces for the Grade II Pianoforte Examination. Teachers and Candidates are STRONGLY ADVISED to consult the Syllabus for the current year. In any event of variation, the Syllabus must be considered authoritative.

The editing of all pieces should be carefully studied but, particularly in the case of pieces in List A, must be considered as helpful and not arbitrary. Phrasing, shading nuances, pedalling, fingering, etc., — which are generally considered to be essential to a good performance — are given only as guides where the composer's own markings are inadequate.

Every effort has been made, in the case of the List A pieces, to base the editing on an original edition of each composition. Whenever possible, consult other editions for comparative purposes.

Where no pedalling is indicated it does not necessarily mean that the pedals should not be used. All metronome speeds are approximate only and should be considered as advisable rather than compulsory.

Naturally, every subtlety of expression cannot be indicated. To come alive music needs, continually, a subtle shading and shaping which responds sensitively to its harmonic and melodic flow. The development, therefore, of personal conviction and taste even in the early years of training is essential in building musicianship.

On page 52 a Glossary is provided of the musical terms found in the compositions of this book.

INDEX

GRADED REQUIREMENTS
PIANO EXAMINATIONS
GRADE II

Candidates must be prepared to play three pieces, one each from Lists A, B and C. (The piece for List C must be chosen from the Inventions in the 1970 edition of the Grade II Pianoforte Examination Book.)

STUDY

Any ONE from the Grade II Pianoforte Examination Book.

TECHNICAL TESTS:

to be played from memory, evenly, with good tone and logical fingering, in the stated keys. All tests to be played ascending and descending. Metronome marks should be regarded as MINIMUM speeds only. Candidates are advised to consult the Royal Conservatory of Music official Technical Requirements Graded Handbook (revised 1966).

SCALES

D, F, G, majors.	Hands separately.	M.M. ♩ = 80
C, G, minors,	Two octaves.	
Harmonic and Melodic.	Eighth notes.	
C, major,	Contrary motion.	
	Eighth notes.	

TRIADS

D, F, G, majors.	Root position and inversions.
C, G, minors.	Hands separately.
	Solid (see Example a)
	Broken (see Example b)
	One octave.
	Moderate tempo.

Example a: (Solid triads)

Example b: (Broken triads)

SIGHT READING

The candidate will be required:

(a) to play a simple four-bar melody, hands separately, with given fingering, in the key of C, F, or G major, in half, quarter, or eighth notes.

(b) to clap or tap a simple rhythmic pattern of two bars in four-four time, with half, quarter, or eighth notes. The following example indicates the approximate degree of difficulty:

EAR TESTS

The candidate will be required:

(a) to clap a simple rhythmic pattern, in two-four or three-four time, clapped twice by the examiner. (The candidate will not be shown the pattern.) The following example indicates the approximate degree of difficulty:

(b) to play a short phrase consisting of up to five consecutive notes, including one change of direction, and possibly an interval of a third. The examiner will play and name the first note, and then play the passage twice. The following example indicates the approximate degree of difficulty:

MINUET IN G MINOR

LIST A

J. S. Bach
(1685 – 1750)

Andante M.M. ♩ = 120

ECOSSAISE

H. L. Hässler
(1564 – 1612)

AIR

J. G. Graeff, Op. 7, No. 4
(1507 – 1576?)

Andante M.M. ♩=112-120

MINUET IN F

LIST A

W. A. Mozart.
(1756 – 1791)

Allegretto M.M. ♩ = 116–126

KING WILLIAM'S MARCH

LIST A

J. Clarke
(1659 – 1707)

Tempo di Marcia M.M. ♩=126-138

CHORALE

LIST A

L. van Beethoven
(1770 – 1827)

MINUET IN C

LIST A

W. A. Mozart
(1756 – 1791)

Allegretto M.M. ♩ = 116–120

GERMAN DANCE

LIST A

L. van Beethoven
(1770 – 1827)

ECOSSAISE

LIST A

J. N. Hummel
(1778 – 1837)

Allegretto M.M. ♩=120-132

MINUET

LIST A

C. P. E. Bach
(1714 – 1788)

CANZONET

LIST A

C. G. Neefe
(1748 – 1798)

Allegretto M.M.♩=100-112
cantabile

SONATINA IN C

T. Haslinger (abridged)
(1787 – 1842)

LIST A

Allegro non tanto M.M. ♩=72

MAY DANCE

LIST A

C. Gurlitt
(1820 – 1901)

Allegretto grazioso M.M. ♩=120-126

MINUET

J. Barrett
(1674 – 1735)

LIST A

Moderato M.M. ♩=120-132

ECOSSAISE IN F

LIST A

L. van Beethoven
(1770 – 1827)

SPOOKS

C. Poole

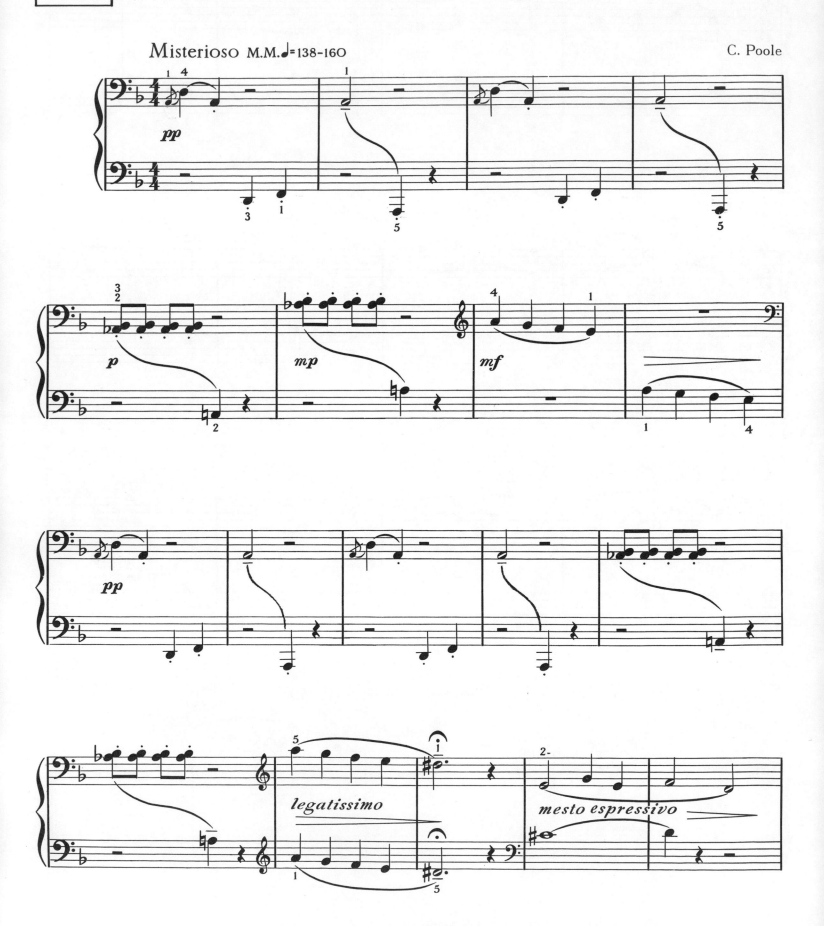

CRADLE SONG

LIST B

Andantino M.M. ♩=56-66

I. Berkovich

SLEEPY OWLS

Andante con moto M.M. ♩=66-72

N. Lubarsky

MARCH OF THE GOBLINS

In March time M.M. ♩=108

B. Berlin

FIREFLIES

LIST B

I. Berkovich

AT THE PLAYGROUND

LIST B

Vivacissimo M.M. ♩=96-100

I. Szelenyi

Used by permission of Editio Musica Budapest — for sale in U.S.A. and Canada

AN OLD DANCE

LIST B

Allegretto M.M. ♩=84-96

L. Barenboim

BOURRÉE

LIST B

Allegro vivace M.M. ♩=88-100

C. Peerson

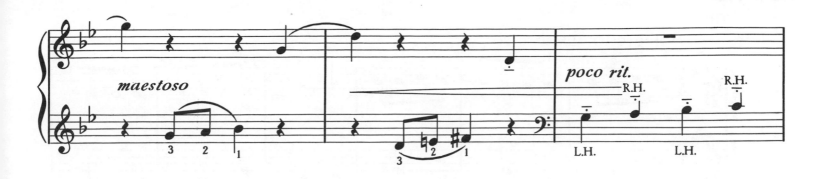

THEME AND VARIATIONS

LIST B

THEME

Allegretto M.M. ♩=76-80

I. Berkovich

VAR. I

Allegretto M.M. ♩=76-80

VAR. II

Andantino M.M. ♩=63

VAR. III

Allegro M.M. ♩=96-100

A LITTLE SONG

LIST B

D. Kabalevsky

COUNTRY DANCE

LIST B

S. Maykapar

Giocoso, energico M.M. ♩=120-138

THE FISHERMAIDEN'S SONG

LIST B

Con moto M.M. ♩=72-76

T. F. Dunhill

DANCE

Allegro M.M. ♩=160-168

A. Goedicke, Op. 36, No. 21

IN THE WOOD

LIST B

Andante M.M. ♩=138–152

C. J. Thomas

WALTZ

Allegro M.M. ♩=160-168

S. Maykapar, Op. 33

PARADE

LIST B

C. Poole

INVENTION NO. 1

I. Shishov

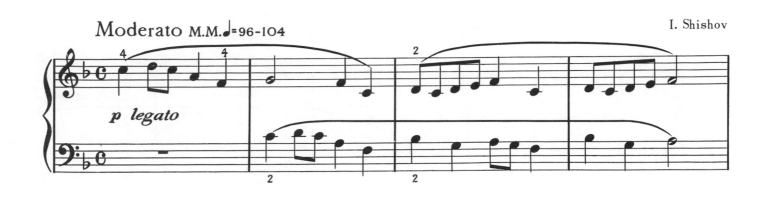

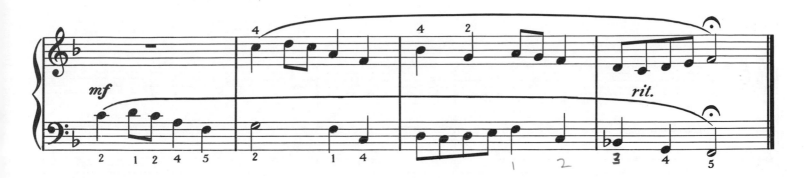

INVENTION NO. 2

A. Karamanov

INVENTION NO. 3

LIST C

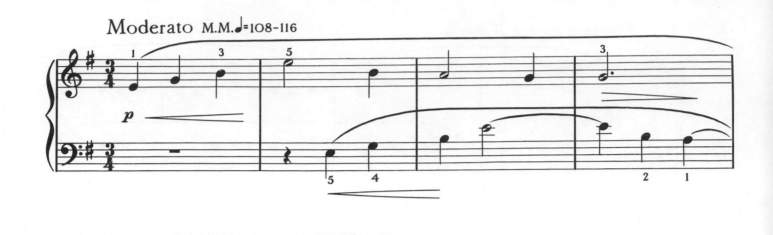

INVENTION NO. 4

LIST C

T. Kenins

Published with permission of composer.

INVENTION NO. 5

LIST C

A. Goldenweiser

INVENTION NO. 6

LIST C

B. Pentland

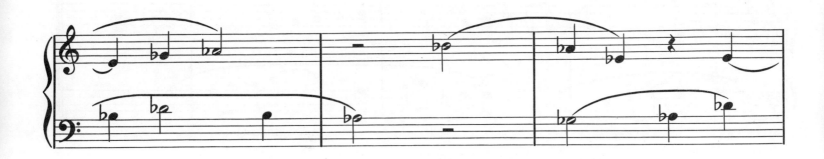

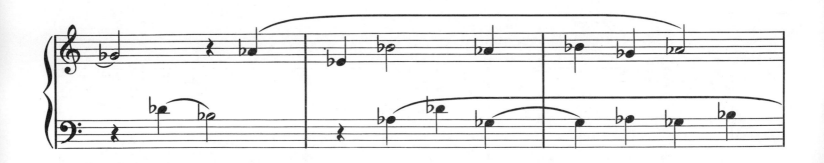

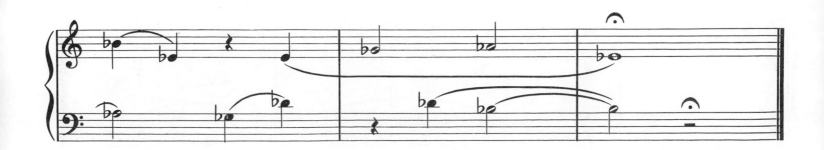

STUDY NO. 1

D. Kabalevsky

STUDY NO. 2

Allegretto M.M. ♩=104-112

I. Berkovich

STUDY NO. 3

Moderato M.M. ♩=112-120

I. Berkovich

STUDY NO. 4

C. J. Thomas

STUDY NO. 5

H. W. Loomis

Moderato grazioso M.M. ♩=112

STUDY NO. 6

A. Goedicke

STUDY NO. 7

STUDY NO. 8

A. Goedicke

Allegro moderato M.M. ♩=69-80

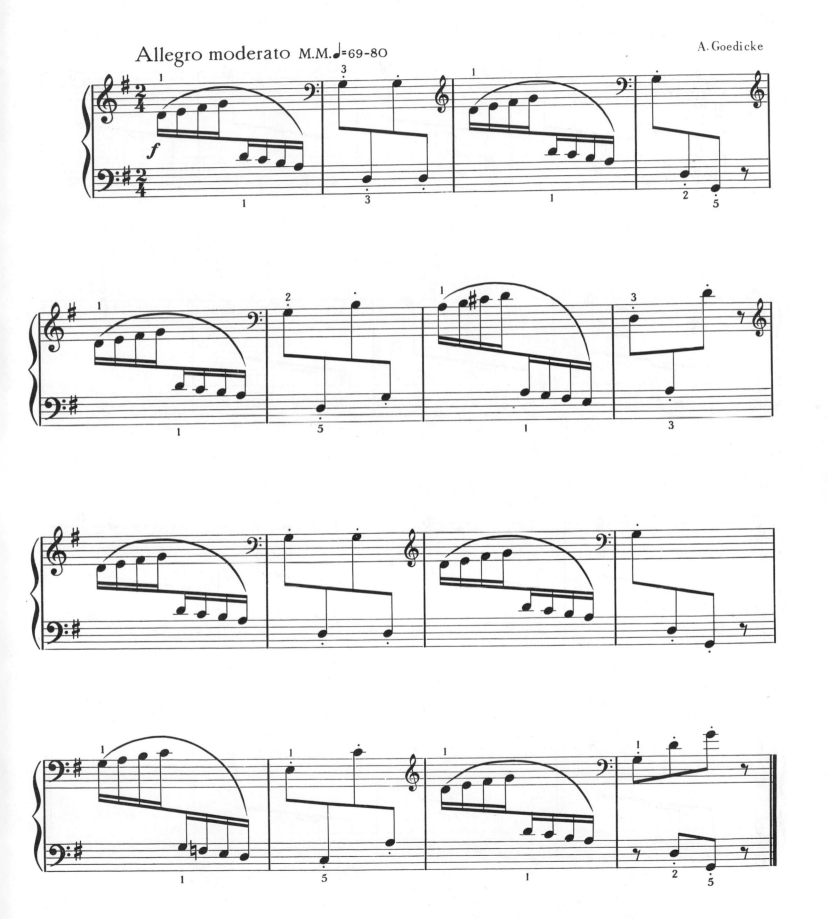

STUDY NO. 9

Vivo M.M. ♩=100–112

D. Kabalevsky

A tempo — in time
Accelerando (accel.) — gradually faster
Agitato — hurried, restless
Air — a short tune, with or without words
Alla Marcia — in march style
Allargando (allarg.) — slower and broader
Allegretto — not too fast or lively
Allegro — quick, happy, lively
Allegro non tanto — not too quickly
Andante — at a moderate walking pace
Bourrée — a lively dance of French origin
Cantabile — in a flowing, singing style
Canzonet — a short song
Chorale — a type of traditional German Hymn
Con — with
Cradle Song — lullaby
Crescendo (cresc.) — becoming gradually louder
Da Capo (D.C.) — repeat from the beginning
D.C. al Fine — return to the beginning and play to the word "Fine"
Decrescendo — becoming gradually softer
Diminuendo (Dim.) — becoming gradually softer
Dolce — sweetly
Ecossaise — a lively country dance
Engergico — with energy
Espressivo — expressively, with colour
Fine — end, finish
Forte (f) — loudly
Fortissimo (ff) — very loudly
Gavotte — a graceful, elegant dance
Giocoso — playfully
Grazioso — gracefully
Legatissimo — very smoothly
Legato — smoothly
Leggiero — lightly
Lento — slowly
L. H. — left hand
Mezzo forte (mf)   moderately loud
Mezzo piano (mp) — moderately soft
Maestoso — majestically
Marcato — well marked
Martellato — with a heavily accented touch
Mesto — sadly, mournfully
Minuet — a dance in triple rhythm
Misterioso — mysteriously
Moderato — at a moderate pace
Molto — much, very
Moto — motion
Musette — a composition with a drone-bass
Piano (p) — softly
Pianissimo (pp) — very softly
Pedale (Ped.) — pedal
Pesante — heavily
Piu — more
Poco — little
Portamento — indicates half-staccato
R.H. — right hand
Rallentando (Rall.) — becoming gradually slower
Ritardando (Rit.) — becoming gradually slower
Scherzando — playfully
Senza — without
Sempre — always
Sforzando (sfz) — strongly accented
Simile — same
Sonatina — a short, easy Sonata
Spirito — with spirit
Staccato — detached, crisply
Subito — suddenly
Tempo di Marcia — in march tempo
Tenuto (ten.) — hold for the full time-value
Una Corda (u.c.) — use the soft pedal
Vivace — lively
Vivacissimo — very lively
Vivo — with life; brisk
Waltz — a dance in triple rhythm

COMMON MUSICAL SIGNS

$\bar{\rho}$ (Portamento) — use a slightly detached touch

$\downarrow$ (Staccato) — use a crisply detached touch

$\downarrow$ (Accent) — stress the note

$\bar{\rho}$ (Sustained) — put a slight stress on the note also

$\Vert$: :$\Vert$ (Repeat) — repeat the passage within the repeat signs

$\overset{\frown}{\rho}$ (Pause) — hold the note longer than its full value

8va ············· play the notes one octave higher than written

8va ············· play the notes one octave lower than written

use the damper pedal, changing it where marked $\wedge$, putting

it down where marked $\llcorner$, and releasing it at $\lrcorner$.